CHOOSING YOUR WAY THROUGH AMERICA'S PAST

BOOK 1

ADVENTURES

from the 1700's

Anne E. Schraff

illustrated by Steven Meyers

J. WESTON WALCH
PUBLISHER

PORTLAND, MAINE

Cover art: © North Wind Picture Archives
The March to Valley Forge

Background: © Erwin Raisz, Landforms of the United States

1   2   3   4   5   6   7   8   9   10

ISBN 0-8251-2614-2

Copyright © 1990, 1991
J. Weston Walch, Publisher
P. O. Box 658 • Portland, Maine 04104-0658

Printed in the United States of America

Contents

Introduction

Most history books focus on famous people and reveal little about what the average person was doing at the time. This book highlights the courage, determination, and plain hard work of ordinary people, and it does so in an unusual way with adventures you participate in. Each adventure casts you as the central character and, at critical junctures, requires you to choose between options. Based on two sets of choices, each adventure has four possible outcomes—some tragic, some triumphant, just as they were for the real people of the times.

Your role is fictional, but the historical details are accurate. Each story is supplemented by a short passage containing interesting facts related to the period, a true/false or matching quiz, and two sets of suggested activities.

Other recommended activities include:

- Reviewing vocabulary before you read each story.

- Keeping a written record of your choices and the consequences of those choices.

- Discussing alternatives with others who chose different courses of action.

- Considering whether the protagonist is male or female. (In the majority of cases, the protagonist is sex-neutral.)

- Analyzing any effects this book has had on the way you make decisions and take risks.

- Writing a report on why it would, or would not, have been fun to live during this period of American history.

This book is intended for enjoyment as well as instruction. We hope that you will find it fun.

ON THE AUCTION BLOCK

It is 1730 and you are a young black slave. The Wall Street auction block is crowded today. You will be sold this hot morning in New York. Next to you are Indians and white people. Some are servants who will be sold to employers. They will be free in seven years or less. You will never be free.

You still remember the Guinea coast of Africa. You were born there. It was green and beautiful. You remember playing by the side of a river with your sister. One awful day you were captured by slave traders. You were put on a large boat. You were chained to the floor of the boat. Oh, how many of you were packed together! You never knew such misery.

When the seas were rough the skin on your elbows was worn to the bone. The food was terrible. You had beans boiled to a pulp and covered with red pepper. They called it slabber-sauce.

Many died of sickness on the boat. Some went crazy. You thought you would lose your mind too. But somehow you made it. When you arrived in the colonies you were sold to a blacksmith. He was an old man who taught you how to repair iron kettles. It was hard, hot work. You longed for freedom though your master wasn't cruel. Then, suddenly, the old man got sick. He closed his blacksmith shop. You were sold, just as his tools were sold. The old man's hammers and tongs and clamps brought a good price. Now you stand on the auction block. You are property, like the tongs that held the glowing hot iron.

You have dreamed sometimes of running away. You might go to another town. Some black people have been freed by their masters. You could pretend you were freed. You might open a small business of your own. You know how to repair kettles.

The slave to your right is a cobbler. Two men are fighting over him. Nobody is looking at you. Because you are a trusted slave, you wear no chains. You could slip into the crowd easily. But it is dangerous. A runaway slave is harshly treated if caught.

■ *If you run, turn to page 3.*

■ *If you stay, turn to page 4.*

Find out what your fate is!

You step quickly behind two white servants. Then you hurry into a milling crowd of black women. They are all house servants. The master allows them to go into town and sell cracked eggs and clams and oysters for pocket change. You smile at them as if nothing is wrong. You are shaking inside, but you walk at a normal pace. You don't want to look like a runaway.

"The blacksmith's slave has run off!" screams a man at the auction block. Oh! You are already missed!

You must hurry along now. You push your way through a crowd of black women and children who sell berries and herbs.

The back door of a tavern is open. You can see many barrels standing there. If you slipped in, you might squeeze between the barrels and crouch down. But then, if the slave catchers enter and search the place, you are trapped. You might be wiser to keep running until you reach the marketplace. Slaves and free men and women of color mingle there. There is always a crowd, and you would be hard to find.

You stop a moment to catch your breath. You are well hidden behind some women who balance huge baskets on their heads. You can tell which of the slaves are from Long Island. Their hair is tied in braids with dried eelskin. The Jersey household slaves have plaited forelocks tied with lead from tea packages. You stare harder at the open tavern door. No one is back there. You would not be seen if you slipped in. And everything looks dusty, as if there is little activity in that back room.

You notice two stout red-faced men coming from the auction block. They have the look of slave catchers. They hunt for you, looking right and left. They have the cruel eyes of wolves.

You can reach the tavern by striding among the noisy clam sellers who shout for customers. Or you could slip behind the herb sellers and then run for all you're worth toward the marketplace.

■ *If you go into the tavern, turn to page 5.*

■ *If you go to the marketplace, turn to page 6.*

You are afraid to escape. Soon a tall, rangy man comes toward you. "Do you know your craft?" he demands.

The man looks cruel and stingy. He will probably lash you if you don't work day and night. But if you purposely act stupid, the auctioneer will punish you. He's a clever man. He knows you came highly praised by your old master.

"I can repair kettles very well," you mutter.

"Speak up, darkie," commands the auctioneer. He jabs you with his walking stick. It brings a sharp pain to your ribs.

"I know blacksmithing," you repeat in a louder voice.

"You better!" grumbles the man. He buys you for a good price. Then he barks at you, "Come along! I haven't got all day!"

You follow the man, whose name is Mr. Devers. Soon you arrive at a noisy blacksmith shop. It is filled with carts and wagons being repaired. You go to a bench in the back where kettles are piled almost to the ceiling.

It's hot and miserable inside the place. You work on the kettles as others mold hot iron into cart wheels and horseshoes.

One day a young Marylander comes in to have a wheel repaired. His wife is with him. She brings a pot with a hole in it. You repair it quickly. She seems very pleased. "We need a good blacksmith on the plantation," the man says.

You look at the man. Would he be a better master? You work hard now for poor food and a dirty straw mat to sleep on. Would life be better in Maryland?

You know you can change the Marylander's mind about buying you if you want to. He seems worried about "slaves who would run off in the night." You need just whisper that once you ran away, though you never did. But if you would fare better in Maryland, you could smile at the Marylander and act the part of a faithful slave.

"I am so desperately in need of a blacksmith," the Marylander says to your master. "I will pay what you paid, plus a handsome bonus."

Your master scratches the stubble on his chin. He knows you are good. But he cannot resist making a profit.

■ *If you make the Marylander favor you, turn to page 7.*

■ *If you do not, turn to page 8.*

You duck into the tavern's back door, crouching down behind some barrels of ale. You hope for the best. A good-sized rat runs across your foot. You make no sound.

"Hey, you!" growls a big, beefy man coming into the back room. "So you're what the hollering out in the street is all about. You're the runaway slave."

You leap up and grapple with the man as you try to flee. He has arms as big as tree trunks! Before you can get away, the slave catchers are here. They have been drawn by the man's shouts.

You are stripped to the waist and tied to a cart. The cart is slowly driven through the city. At each corner the cart stops and you are given eleven lashes on your bare back. Little groups of black men and women watch sadly. The selling of cracked eggs and clams stops. Your cruel lashing is a lesson for them too. This is what happens to a runaway slave!

"Look on, you slaves!" shouts the brute who whips you. "Mind your masters and do their will. If you run off, you are a thief. They own you as they own their plows. The runaway slave is a thief who steals from the master."

Stinging pain goes through your body. Blood runs down your back.

Finally you are dragged back to the auction block.

"No good master wants an unruly slave," the auctioneer tells you, "So you will be sold as a field laborer."

His words come true. You are bought by a harsh man who takes you to a plantation where other slaves work. The others are unskilled. You all must labor at hard, back-breaking work from dawn to dusk. The overseer rides his mule up and down the fields, slashing at anyone who slows down. His whip falls often on your aching back.

One night you decide you can take it no longer. You try to run away again. You are too weary to outrun your pursuers. You are savagely beaten.

You crawl to a straw mat and lie down. You dream of your childhood home in Africa. You remember the bamboo roof covered with palm leaves. Delicious fruit grew in the forest. You loved the cool, sweet coconut milk. Your memories bring a smile to your face.

You are found dead in the morning.

■ *Turn to page 9.*

You hide in the crowd, then turn a corner and sprint off. As you near the marketplace, you spot a kindly black face. "Please, may I carry one of your baskets of fish?" you ask. The woman smiles and nods. Soon you are clutching a basket and shouting, "Fresh fish, clams!"

You flow into the marketplace, mingling quickly with slaves and freed blacks. The men who are pursuing you stand at the edge of the crowd staring in confusion. You have borrowed a floppy straw hat from a child and you carry the basket, shouting, "Clams, oysters! Get your fresh clams and oysters!"

When night falls, you are still free! You have a little money from your old master. (He would give you money to buy supplies. When you got a bargain, you pocketed the leftover coins.) You buy new clothes and keep moving.

When you reach Middletown, you find a small blacksmith shop. You ask the man if he needs a helper. "My old master died. He set me free before crossing over the River Jordan."

The young blacksmith nods. "If you are skilled, I can use you. I have work enough for four helpers."

You work as hard as you did as a slave. But you receive a wage. You are happier than you have been since leaving Africa. Every coin you receive, you turn over and over in your hand. It is like a piece of gold. You cannot believe this is yours! You can spend it as you wish!

As time goes by, you are less afraid of being caught. You marry a freed slave and start a family of your own. You take the money you have saved and buy a small farm far out from a village. As each child is born, you feel new joy. Your children are not slaves. They are free!

Your son is one of the black soldiers with General George Washington when he crosses the Delaware in 1776. He fights for American independence and you are very proud. The only thing that makes you sad is that most black people are still slaves.

You hope that someday soon all slaves will be free. In the meantime, you make the best of your life. And it is a very good life indeed. You are never sorry that you made that daring break for freedom.

■ *Turn to page 9.*

The Marylander seems kinder than your present master. So you smile graciously and promise to work hard. He quickly pays your master the bonus. And soon you are riding in the back of a wagon. Mr. and Mrs. Jeffers are taking you to their plantation.

When you get to the plantation you see many beautiful Arabian horses. Some are white and others chestnut. Mr. Jeffers loves to race horses.

You learn to shoe horses and do the other repair work on the plantation. You are glad you came here. The Jeffers family is very kind and you enjoy the horses. Sometimes it is your duty to exercise the horses. It's a fine feeling to ride across the countryside with the Jeffers children. Sometimes you even forget that you are a slave!

Then, suddenly, disaster strikes! Mr. Jeffers dies of a summer fever and Mrs. Jeffers goes almost mad. The children are sent away to grandparents. You are to be sold!

What a shock this is to you. You have grown to feel like one of the family. You cannot believe they would sell you! Why, you have been with this family for fourteen years. You have had many pleasant times here. Have they no feeling for you at all?

The oldest son of the Jeffers family is David, who is seventeen. "Master David," you plead, "I will do any kind of work. Please don't sell me off. I am older now. I cannot endure hard field work."

"You are skilled. You will go to a good place," David says. But you can see that he really does not care. He is grief-stricken because of his father's death. He worries about his mother. What are you to him?

"Master David," you continue to plead, "don't you remember how I taught you to ride when you were small?"

The young man grows angry. "Do not hound me! I have the plantation to sell. I have stock to sell! I cannot be harried by the woes of a slave!"

Your worst fears come true. You are sold to a cruel man at a neighboring plantation. The overseer is a brutal devil. You must work until you drop from weariness.

You die at an early age, worn out by misuse.

■ *Turn to page 9.*

You decide your best chance is to stay where you are. Mr. Devers is a hard man, but he is teaching you a lot.

You mention your dreams of running away and Mr. Jeffers, the Marylander, hurries off.

You put up with your bad food and dirty sleeping mat and you work hard. You learn every task in the blacksmith shop. Eventually you are better than your master at almost everything.

"You're a clever one," he says one day. "I did not think someone of your race could learn so well."

"Thank you," you say.

One day, after five years, a wagon slips and falls on Mr. Devers. You and another slave lift it off him, saving him from being crushed to death. He recovers from his severe injuries, but he is now crippled. The pain and helplessness he now suffers have changed him. With watery eyes he calls you to his side one morning. He is sitting on a stool mending a pot. "You have been with me a long time. You and the other darkie saved my life after the accident. You see the condition I am in. I cannot do my work. I can trust no one but you two to take care of my business."

"Yes, Master," you say.

"I wake in pain and I lie down at night in pain. I am not long for this world. Will you stick with me until I die? I will set you free in my will. Will you take the bargain?"

"Yes, Master, I will," you say.

You work for another four years. Mr. Devers is often as mean as before. But now it is easier to forgive him. He suffers very much. When he dies, you find he has kept his promise. He leaves you your freedom and a small sum of money. It's enough for you to open a small blacksmith shop of your own.

You marry a free person of color and soon must hire other workers. You build a small home for your growing family. You always thought you could never be happy here. You dreamed of Africa. You longed to go home to that good green land. But now, when you buy a small farm and settle down, you are happy.

You sit under your fruit trees in your old age and play with your grandchildren. And always you say to those children, "What a blessing freedom is! Be thankful for it! Always be thankful that you are free!"

■ *Turn to page 9.*

The Amazing Poet

A little black slave girl named Phillis was brought from Senegal in Africa about 1761. She was eight years old. She was bought by a family in Boston. Little Phillis was a maid in the Wheatley family. But soon John Wheatley and his wife saw how smart Phillis was. She learned English very quickly.

When Phillis was fourteen, she began to write poetry. Her poems were so good that they were published. One of Phillis's poems was about George Washington. He read it and liked it very much. He told Phillis that her poem was "elegant." He said she had great talent and she was a genius. George Washington signed his letter, "Your obedient humble servant, George Washington."

Young Phillis Wheatley (she took the name of her master) was a special girl. She overcame slavery and left her mark on history.

Matching

1. Phillis was from _____ .
2. The big slave market was at _____ .
3. Beans with red pepper was called _____ .
4. The name of the family who owned

   Phillis was _____ .
5. Phillis lived in _____ .

a) slabbersauce
b) Wheatley
c) Senegal
d) Boston
e) Wall Street

Group Activities

1. Using maps, find the routes of slave ships across the Atlantic. Some were part of what was called triangular trade. Most slaves were captured on the west coast of Africa and then brought to the West Indies. From there they were brought to cities like Boston.

2. The slaves were brought over on ships crammed with people. Each adult person was crowded into a space about sixteen inches high, two and one-half feet wide, and six feet long. Measure such a space and imagine living in such a way for six to eight weeks.

3. Using geography and other reference books, find the west coast of Africa, where many slaves came from. What is happening there now in countries like Senegal and Guinea? Make reports to the class.

Individual Activities

1. Phillis Wheatley's poems were like other popular poems of the time. Find one of her poems and read it.

2. Imagine you are a runaway slave. Write a description of a wild adventure as you dash to freedom.

3. Write a short paper on one of the following former slaves in American history:

Peter Salem   Frederick Douglass
Harriet Tubman   Robert Smalls

SERVANT FOR SALE

It's 1760 and life is hard and mean for the poor in England. You have not been able to get an education. London is full of crime. Everywhere you look, mobs fight. You are afraid to go out at night. Thieves are hung in public, but it doesn't help. As the crowds watch the hangings, pockets are picked by other thieves. You want to find a better life in the American colonies. But you have no money for your passage.

"Go as an indentured servant," a friend suggests. "The rich in the colonies always need servants."

"But what must I promise?" you ask.

"Seven years of work and then you are free."

You look into the idea. You find out that for seven years you cannot marry without permission. You cannot leave day or night without asking. You will get room and board for seven years.

You decide it's your only chance for a good future. You dread the long sea voyage, but you must put up with it.

You are shocked when you board the ship. You must sleep on a bed two feet wide and six feet long. There are over six hundred people on the ship. But the worst is yet to come!

The water you must drink is filthy. It's black and thick with dirt and worms. The meat is highly salted and half rotten. The biscuits are full of red worms and spiders' nests.

During the voyage you suffer from scurvy for lack of fresh fruit or vegetables. Your mouth is sore with mouth-rot. During storms, the waves are as tall as mountains. Your ship is tossed about like a toy.

Among the small children on board, measles and dysentery break out. On one Sunday five little ones are buried at sea.

At last the terrible voyage is over. Weak and thin, you stumble ashore. Now you must decide which job to take. The man who paid your passage will send you to his shopkeeper brother in Charles Town in South Carolina. (You have heard the weather is beastly hot there.) Or you can work for the Boston shipbuilder in his own home. Boston has a climate more like England.

■ *If you go to Charles Town, turn to page 13.*

■ *If you work in Boston, turn to page 14.*

Find out what your fate is!

You arrive in Charles Town in South Carolina and like it at once. The streets are broad and pretty. Flowers are blooming everywhere. How different it is from London!

Your master has a thirteen-room brick house, a stable, and a carriage house. There must be a lot of work here! You hope you don't have to do it all! And do you also have to clean the stables?

Quickly, you find that your fears come true. You must work like a slave. Nothing you do suits your master, Mr. Phelps, nor his wife. You must polish the silver. But it never shines enough to please Mrs. Phelps. She scolds constantly. You must amuse the children, but they are spoiled. You must repair their hobbyhorses and dolls.

In May of the next year a fierce hurricane strikes Charles Town. The winds howl and the violent rain pounds down. You are terrified. It is much more frightening even than the storms on your sea voyage. Then, when the sun comes out, everything is a mess.

"We must clean up at once." Mr. Phelps demands. "We must work twice as hard to make things right. My wife cannot bear disorder."

You drag fallen branches into a pile for burning. You sweep and scrub until you are numb. Your back aches so much you think it is broken.

Mrs. Phelps sits on the porch fanning herself. She yells directions to you. "You missed that branch there! Can't you sweep a bit faster? Look at all those leaves!"

You cannot bear much more! You dream of running away. But you are bound by a contract. You are like a slave. If you ran, they could hunt you down. And you have no money either.

You sit down for a minute to get your breath. Suddenly there is Mrs. Phelps with the broom. She gives you a nasty blow across your cheek. "Lazy wretch! Do you think you are here to lie about?" she screams at you.

Rage reddens your face. Your blood boils. A plot comes to your mind. You could steal some silver and escape to another city. But dare you do such a thing? You feel you have been unjustly treated. It would be no crime if you stole a few silver spoons and left.

■ *If you flee with the silver, turn to page 17.*

■ *If you remain here, turn to page 18.*

You arrive in Boston and stare at the hills rising from the harbor. You see many churches. The shipbuilder is Aaron Phelps. He's cheerful and funny. You like him.

But you soon learn he does not build ships anymore. "The ship business went bad," he tells you as you ride to his home in a carriage. "I'm a privateer now."

"Is that like a pirate?" you ask.

He roars with laughter. "My armed ships only attack French and Spanish ships. We are British folk. They are foes. So last year I got fifty chests of Spanish silver and gold, eh?"

"Is it dangerous?" you ask.

"Aye!" he says, showing you his left hand, which is missing all its fingers. "A Spanish sword did this."

You will live in a small brick house with the privateer and his son. You must do the cooking and cleaning. But the two men are not very demanding. It should be an easy job.

One night you are out late shopping for meat. You see your master arguing loudly with another man. They quickly come to blows in the dusky lane behind a vendor's closed stall. Your master strikes a blow and the other fellow slumps down. Your master looks around nervously. He wonders if anyone has seen the deed. You have, but you hide from his glance. You don't want any trouble.

Is the other fellow dead? Have you seen a murder?

Trembling with fear, you hurry home. What will you do if the constable comes and asks questions? Should you tell the truth and make trouble for your kind master? Or must you lie and protect a criminal?

That night you toss and turn with worry. Every sound hits you like a blow. Even the wind banging the shutters startles you. Then, around midnight, there is a pounding on the door.

"Open up, Phelps!" thunders a man's voice. It must be the constable. They have found the dead man. Now you will be questioned! You must escape through the window before the constable sees you. But then you are a fugitive. And where will you run to? You have a contract that says you must remain here. You don't want to break the law.

■ *If you run, turn to page 15.*

■ *If you remain, turn to page 16.*

Quickly dressing, you run to the window. Opening it, you climb out, fleeing into the darkness. You peer around the corner and see a mob of men at your master's door. Oh! They are not lawmen at all! It looks like a bunch of tough, dangerous thugs. Maybe they have come to avenge the death of their friend at the vendor's stall.

Your master is alone in the house. His son is away. You must do something!

You race into the darkness. You do not stop running until you reach a church. You wake up the parson and tell him what has happened.

"We shall call the constable at once," the parson says, hurrying with you to the law.

It is too late! When you get to the house, your master is dead. The fight you saw at the vendor's stall was a brawl with a gang member. What is Boston coming to? The parson shakes his head sadly. "People used to be safe in their own homes. Now gangs of thieves are about in the night."

You continue working for your master's son. But the house is a sad place now.

On a hot day in September, the men who killed your master are hanged. You stand in a crowd of about a thousand people to watch. Soon after, posters are made telling of the crime. The posters describe the wicked lives of the hanged men. The posters say:

"Beware, young people, and look at these men before it is too late."

You shudder and go home.

For seven years you work for the son of Aaron Phelps. Then you are free. You leave Boston and work for a while for wages in Maryland. Then you buy a small farm.

After you marry and have children, you tell them of the day you saw the hanging.

"I was a young person then, and it was a frightening thing," you say. "I hope you never have to see such a sight."

You sometimes think of what might have happened if you had not run away from your master's house. You went for help, but what if you had stayed? Could you have saved Aaron Phelps?

■ *Turn to page 19.*

You remain in your room, listening at the door. Your master shouts, "Thieves! Felons!"

You look out the side window and see a rabble at the door! "We'll do you in, matey, for the beating you gave one of our lads!" Now you understand. Your master was the victim of one of Boston's gangs of robbers. The thug who now shouts threats is a criminal! And they are battering down the door.

"I have sent for the constable!" you yell. "He is on his way!" You throw on your clothes and leap out the window screaming, "Help! Get the constable!"

The men of the Boston South Watch (police) arrive in the nick of time. There is not a moment to lose. It's a fierce battle. The thieves have swords, but the constable and his men overcome them.

In the early dawn, your master grabs your hand and says, "I would be dead now except for you! I owe you my very life."

"You have been kind to me. I could not do otherwise," you say.

"One of the gang tried to pick my pocket today and I whipped him. The ones who came tonight would have killed me for that," Mr. Phelps says.

"I'm glad I could help," you tell Aaron Phelps.

"I came within a hair's breadth of death. Now I shall reward you! You are free of your contract at once. If you stay with me I will pay you good wages!" your master says.

You remain with Aaron Phelps another two years. By then you have a tidy sum of money. You open a cook shop. You are open every morning at ten. Many of the houses have no ovens, so they bring their dinners to you. You bake the food for them. You charge one shilling and three pence per dish. Also, you sell bread and hot rolls. Soon you have a fine catering business.

You find a huge home to buy and soon you hire people to do your work. You own a hundred acres and have a fine garden and terraces, even canals. You have a deer park where wild deer graze for your amusement. You give grand parties which are attended by all the important people.

How far you have come from that awful ship and biscuits full of spiders' webs!

■ *Turn to page 19.*

In the dead of night, with a sack of silver spoons, you leave the house. You look back a lot as you run. It is a bad feeling to think someone is chasing you. You remember a few weeks ago when an escaping black slave came through here. She was caught and savagely punished. Her screams still haunt you. She was branded with a hot iron. Surely a runaway indentured servant would not suffer such a cruel fate, and yet . . .

"There goes the wretch!" comes a shout as you run by the stables. One of the Phelps children was lurking there! In another moment you are caught by other servants and dragged back to the house. The bag of stolen silver convicts you. Your master glares at you.

"You shall suffer the pains due a thief!" he shouts. He calls the city constable, and you are quickly taken away. Justice is swift. You are put in a prison in Charles Town. It has six rooms, twelve square feet each. In each small room sixteen prisoners are crowded. Men and women are packed in together. There is not even room to lie down! One of your companions in prison is a murderer! The others are mostly poor souls who owe money. How bitterly you regret taking the silver!

You are sentenced to four years in this terrible prison. You plead for a lighter sentence. Because of your youth, the judge agrees. He will let you off with a branding of your hand. A *T* is to be burned into your hand. For a few minutes, the pain is awful. Then, for days, your hand is terribly sore. The worst part of it is that wherever you go, people will know you are a thief.

You work at any job you can find. You help a vendor load fish. You sell oysters from a stall. Finally you have enough money to open a small garden-seed shop. At last your life improves a little.

You wear a bandage on your hand and explain it is an old injury. You gain the trust of customers and friends. Little by little you forget the past. But you never forget the terrible mistake you made.

All in all, you were lucky. Several of the other prisoners in that Charles Town prison died of starvation. You got the chance to make a fresh start.

■ *Turn to page 19.*

Bitter though the work is, you remain. You continue to work hard.

The next spring you become friends with the oldest Phelps child. You are about the same age. When you have free time you go riding together. Though you are an indentured servant, and your friend is the child of rich parents, you have much in common. You both love to go out in the countryside. You watch the great cranes playing in the sand dunes. You laugh at the rice birds in the reeds. Sometimes you carry your lunch and eat under the trees.

You tell your friend about your voyage across the sea.

"How brave it was to come such a long way! I was born here. I have not been far from Charles Town. You are much braver than I!" says your friend.

Even Mrs. Phelps begins to treat you with more kindness. It is because of her child. When the master of the house gives a large dinner, you become a guest! You can sit down at the table and eat the ham and duck dinner. No running about, serving. No cleaning up afterwards! You have the chance to eat those delicate fruit tarts and custards and jellies you used only to stare at!

By the next winter, you and the eldest Phelps child plan a wedding. You will be married in the spring. The wedding will be large and festive. All the important people of Charles Town will come to the wedding.

Once you are married, you become a member of this wealthy family. You ride in carriages and leave Charles Town in the summer to escape the heat. You plan dinner parties and help pick out horses to buy.

One day a young indentured servant comes from England to work for you and your spouse. The frightened young Londoner is polishing your silver as you once did. He rubs at it furiously to get it bright. "Is this all right?" he asks you.

You look at the silver and smile. "Yes, indeed," you say. And then you tell him how you too came here as an indentured servant. "I was bonded as you are."

"You?" gasps the servant.

"Indeed," you say with great laughter. "I'll tell you, this is an amazing land!"

■ *Turn to page 19.*

Pirates of the Eighteenth Century

During the 1700s, pirates roamed the seas. They were called buccaneers. Sometimes they served their country. English pirates become heroes by attacking Spanish ships. But most pirates were just thieves who worked for themselves. Among them were two women pirates, Mary Read and Anne Bonny.

Bonny was born in Ireland. She moved with her father to South Carolina as a child. She met a pirate named Calico Jack. Soon she fought beside him with pistol and cutlass.

Mary Read was a poor child. She was forced to dress as a boy so she could get boys' jobs. She was a sailor on a ship captured by pirates. She decided to be a pirate too. Soon she was as fierce a pirate as any man.

Bonny and Read were pirates on the same ship. They were captured around 1720. All the male pirates were hung, but Anne and Mary were spared. Mary soon died of a fever, but nobody knows what happened to Anne Bonny.

Matching

1. Anne Bonny was born in

   _____ .

2. Mary and Anne were captured in

   _____ .

3. Life in London was hard in

   _____ .

4. Indentured servants worked for

   _____ .

5. Red worms were found in

   _____ .

a) seven years

b) Ireland

c) sea biscuits

d) 1720

e) 1760

Group Activities

1. Using a map, find the favorite pirate havens of Captain Kidd, Blackbeard, and Jean Lafitte. The Kidd area was around Newport. The Blackbeard area was between the James River and the Pamlico River. The Lafitte area was from Galveston to New Orleans.

2. The colonial cities had a lot of crime. Justice was harsh and speedy. As a class, decide on fair penalties for people guilty of these common crimes of the 1700s:
   - Footpadding (armed robbery) Failing to pay a debt
   - Picking pockets   Killing someone in a brawl

3. Was it just that Mary Read and Anne Bonny were spared while the men were killed? Debate this. Then vote on what you think is fair.

Individual Activities

1. Write a paragraph about one of the following famous pirates:
   Captain Kidd   Blackbeard   Jean Lafitte

2. Imagine you are on a ship bound for the colonies in 1760. Describe a day on the ship.

3. Supposing in the story you had been a black slave instead of an indentured servant. Did anything happen to you as a servant that could not have happened to you as a slave? Describe it.

SONS OF LIBERTY

It's 1765 and you are a small colonial merchant. You sit in a coffee house with your partner. He's red in the face with anger. "Blast that King George!" he shouts. "Does he think we are made of money?"

You stare into your coffee. You are angry too. You are also worried. You and your partner ship molasses from the West Indies. Now the British are taxing the molasses. Your business could be ruined.

How you and your friends hate British taxes! You must soon put British tax stamps on all your bills. Even playing cards will need stamps. "They will squeeze us to death with their taxes," you groan.

Every day you hear more talk about rebellion.

"We ought to just take up arms and throw the British out," your partner says.

"Oh, but I fear a bloody rebellion," you say.

"It's not right that England should rule us. They are too far away. They know nothing of our problems. They just know how to tax us. Tax, tax, tax!" your partner exclaims.

The little group of merchants around you shouts, "Hear! Hear! Away with the British! We have no need of them. If they won't go willingly, we ought to toss them into the sea!"

"Listen," your partner says. "There's a group of brave youth called the 'Sons of Liberty.' They'll teach those British a lesson. We ought to do for them what we can. They need fighters. They need people to pass out propaganda leaflets."

"But that is rebellion," you say. "That is treason against the British king who rules over us. A colonist who gets into that could hang!"

"What is worse than the tyranny we live under?" your partner says. "I say help the Sons of Liberty any way we can. We must not put stamps on our bills. We ought to burn them!"

You have always been a good citizen. You hate the idea of a rebellion. But your partner is right. The taxes are making it too hard to make a living.

■ If you help the Sons of Liberty, turn to page 23.

■ If you don't, turn to page 24.

Find out what your fate is!

You find a meeting of the Sons of Liberty. It's in the back room of a tavern. An angry-looking man is making a fierce speech.

"We shall teach Colonel Colden a good lesson!" shouts Isaac Sears, a shipmaster.

"Aye, we shall indeed!" another man yells in agreement.

The hair on the back of your neck stands up. This is it! You are making a fateful choice. When you join the Sons of Liberty you are a traitor to England. England is your country. You have always been loyal to her. You stand on the edge of treason!

"Are you with me?" cries Sears. He seems to be staring right at you. The eyes of your friends and neighbors are on you too. The air is electric with hot fury.

"I am with you!" you shout. You are clapped on the back by your friends.

"Always knew you had courage," says a merchant at your side.

You are soon part of an angry mob. You march toward Colonel Colden's house. He has been warned and rushes off to a British warship.

"The coward!" yells Isaac Sears. "Come on! He shall not escape our wrath!"

Led by a shouting, screaming Sears, you reach Colden's coach house. You begin hacking his carriages into wreckage. You force the British officers there to burn sheets of stamps. You have mixed feelings. You want to teach the British a lesson. But will this night of violence never end? It's a new and awful activity for you. You are smashing the belongings of another person. You feel like a criminal.

Isaac Sears jumps atop a smashed carriage. "Let's go to Chambers and Warren streets. There's another British officer there. He has bragged that he will shove the Stamp Act down our throats. Let us see how easy that will be!"

You don't want any more destruction. You would just like to go home. But dare you leave now? Will you seem like a coward?

■ *If you go on with the others, turn to page 25.*

■ *If you go home, turn to page 26.*

You cannot see why all this can't be settled peacefully. When the British see how angry the colonists are, they will give up on these awful taxes.

"I will not take a stand against England," you say. "She is our mother country. I am no traitor."

"Faugh!" cries your partner. "You stand against your friends and neighbors!"

Your friendship with your partner ends. You sell your half of the business. Then you start a new business of your own. You still hate the taxes, but you are not sorry about your choice. Quickly you lose other friends. You lose customers too. It seems that everybody is taking sides. Either you are for the Sons of Liberty or you are for England. It is impossible to keep friendships going if you take opposite sides on this big question.

One day you are having dinner with a friend. He wants to remain loyal to England too. "I want no part of this rebel business. Vandals and criminals! That's all they are. We shall soon smooth over our trouble with England."

You enjoy a fine feast of turtle soup and jellies, sweetmeats, and trifle (a wine-soaked sponge cake covered with whipped cream).

"I'm sure you are right. Good times will return to the colonies. And we shall always remain loyal to England!" you say. You touch glasses, shouting, "To our lasting friendship with England!"

"To the King!" your friend says.

Your glasses clink. Then your window glass shatters. Broken glass lies all over the floor. Someone has thrown a stone through your window!

Terror whitens your friend's face. "The Sons of Liberty! They know our loyalties, my friend. Knaves! Fools!"

"Low criminals, rabble!" you shout. You peer through the open window. It's worse than you feared. A mob has gathered before your house!

"Go back to England, Tories [Tories were Americans loyal to England.]!" screams one enraged man.

"Or we'll burn your houses down! We'll give you the thrashing of your lives!" another threatens.

You are now very frightened. You know some of the people who threaten you now. They used to be your friendly neighbors! Perhaps you should go to England until the trouble blows over.

■ *If you go to England, turn to page 27.*

■ *If you stay, turn to page 28.*

You don't want to be called a coward. Besides, these Sons of Liberty may be right. If they can scare the British, maybe the taxes will be lowered.

You near the house of the British officer. He has run away. Someone warned him that an angry mob was coming. Isaac Sears laughs. "Let's see how the British gentleman lives," he shouts.

You smash down the front door. Soon the sound of splintering wood and cracking glass is all around you. One of your companions knocks a grandfather's clock down. What a noise it makes! It pains you to see the beautiful piece of furniture smashed. You shudder at the vandalism.

"Well, what do we do with all this fine china?" asks Sears.

"The way they tax us, we can't have such china," a man says. He picks up a plate and hurls it against the opposite wall. You pick up a delicate china cup. You smash it against the wall too. You think of your mother's china. You dread what she would say if she saw you now. You really don't like this business at all. You hope it will do some good, but you are not sure.

You smash a beautiful ladder-back chair.

Now some of your companions are drinking liquor they found. They grow even more wild. They go out into the garden. Now they begin to pull up flowering shrubs!

The last thing they do is tear books apart. That shocks you the most. You have always respected books. But you help throw the books into the street.

You are sickened by the ugliness of it all. If only this awful night frightens the British into changing their harsh laws!

But the troubles only grow worse. In 1770 a group of young Bostonians begins throwing snowballs and rocks at British soldiers. The British fire at the Bostonians. Several men die. It is called the Boston Massacre. You now know that war will come. The colonies must fight England for their independence. You will join in the fight. You have made your decision.

You risk your life and all you have for American independence.

■ *Turn to page 29.*

You slip away in the darkness. You cannot smash another home. The poor devil who owns it has done nothing personally to you! Your parents did not raise a vandal!

In the morning, your partner taunts you. "You had no stomach for what needed to be done, eh?" he says.

"I cannot believe that smashing another person's home will gain anything," you say.

"We shall have no homes ourselves pretty soon. These vile taxes will cost us everything we have. Tell the truth! You were afraid, afraid to stand with the Sons of Liberty!"

"Lies! Foul lies!" you shout.

"Then come with us tonight. We shall teach another British tax hound a lesson!"

"No," you mutter. Soon you break up your partnership. You move to Boston to make a fresh start. You hope the troubles blow over. You just want peace and quiet.

For a few years it looks as though there might be peace. The British lift some of the hated laws. Maybe they have seen their folly.

It is 1770 and you are walking on a chill evening in March. You are near the Custom House on King Street. A single British sentry is standing guard. Suddenly he is pelted with snowballs.

You turn to see a crowd of young people. They are throwing the snowballs and yelling insults at the British guard. Other British soldiers come on the run.

One of the crowd taunting the British is a tall black fellow. He's about six feet two inches with short, curly hair. The others are mulattoes and Irish sailors.

Suddenly the British fire their guns. You see the black fellow fall. A gasp goes through the crowd.

"Crispus Attucks is dead!" someone shouts. He was the black man. Now, quickly, four more fall dead.

Samuel Adams of the Sons of Liberty calls this the Boston Massacre. Everybody is angry. Now war will surely break out. You must fight for American independence. Even though you hoped for peace, it is now impossible. You quickly join the other American colonists who go to war.

■ *Turn to page 29.*

Sadly you sell your property and sail to England. You feel very bitter. But at least you and your family will be safe and peaceful.

Within a few years war breaks out between England and the American colonies. Your oldest son is in the British army sent to the colonies. He fights under Cornwallis at Princeton during a bitter cold January. It's a full-scale firefight. The night fills with acrid smoke. It stings your son's eyes and chokes his throat.

You learn the details of this battle from your son's fellow-soldier.

"Your son was charging with his bayonet. He killed two colonial soldiers," the letter says.

You are gripped with sorrow. You lean back in your chair. Your eyes fill with tears.

"Suddenly a gun butt knocked your son down. He was on his knees. He did not murmur. But I could see he was in great pain. He did not suffer long. His last words were of his love for you. He died in an orchard," says the letter.

You have never felt such sadness. You think back on the happy times you spent in the colonies. You raised your children there. You felt like an American.

You wonder: Did the sons of old friends and neighbors kill your son? Did your son kill the sons of old friends and neighbors?

What a sad thing that it had to come to this!

You cannot make a new life in England, and you return eventually to the United States. You look at your son's grave, then you go west and farm. After a while your sorrow is less. You have a prosperous farm and once again you feel a part of this new land.

You only wish your son could enjoy it too.

■ *Turn to page 29.*

You will not be run out of this land! Just because you are loyal to England, you won't be chased out. You won't be a traitor, that's all!

As the bitterness against England grows, you find it harder to live in your city. Mobs attack your house. They stone your carriage when war breaks out.

You try to keep out of trouble. But then there's a rumor that you are a spy for the British. When some colonial soldiers are caught, you are blamed. A mob surrounds your house.

"Come out, Tory spy," they demand.

You get your family out the back door. Then you leap on a horse to escape. The mob blocks your way. You are dragged from the horse. "I am no spy!" you shout.

"You are a Tory! You stand with King George, the foul tyrant!" the leader of the mob cries. You are stripped of your clothing and bound. Then you are plunged to your neck into a barrel of molasses. They even pour molasses into your hair! After that they roll you in a pile of chicken feathers! What a sticky, horrible mess you are! They load you in a wagon and go down to the tavern. Everyone comes out to make fun of you.

Worse yet, the molasses draws flies. The big green flies buzz around your head. They are soon stuck to the molasses, on your head and in your hair. Flies crawl at will over your face. Your tormentors laugh at your misery.

Finally the wicked men let you go. You clean yourself up and flee with your family. For the rest of the war you hide in the wilderness of Kentucky, fishing and trapping.

After the war you slip back into Philadelphia. You take up your life again. Happily, few hold grudges. Hardly anyone talks about the war. Everybody is too busy building the new country. You open a large hardware store and become rich. You do much better than you did before the war. You are glad that the United States won its independence, even though you were on the other side.

The main thing now is that you are all Americans again.

■ *Turn to page 29.*

The Adams Family

Samuel "Sam" Adams was a fiery revolutionary. He had a gift for getting people all stirred up. He helped the Sons of Liberty start rebellion in the colonies. When the Boston Massacre happened, Sam Adams made the most of it. He said the British soldiers killed innocent people on purpose.

John Adams was Sam's cousin. He did not agree with Sam's story about the British soldiers. When the British soldiers were brought to trial, John Adams defended them. John said the soldiers didn't mean to kill anybody. They were just defending themselves against a mob. The British soldiers were found innocent.

But when war came, the Adams cousins stood together for American independence. Sam signed the Declaration of Independence. John became the second president of the United States.

True/False

_____ 1. Sam Adams defended the British soldiers involved in the Boston Massacre.

_____ 2. The British taxed molasses from the West Indies.

_____ 3. Sam and John Adams were brothers.

_____ 4. The Sons of Liberty wanted to obey the tax laws.

_____ 5. Sam Adams signed the Declaration of Independence.

Group Activities

1. Read about the details of the Boston Massacre in several library books. Then one group of students presents the side of the British soldiers. Another group presents the side of the colonists. The class votes on a verdict.

2. Acting as members of the Sons of Liberty, make large propaganda posters to display in class.

3. Discuss in class the hard choice a colonist had to make at this time. If he was loyal to England (as he always had been, considering himself an Englishman), he was disloyal to his neighbors. If she was disloyal to England, she was committing treason.

Individual Activities

1. Write a paragraph about one of the following:
   Samuel Adams   Crispus Attucks   John Adams   King George III

2. "Gravestone rubbing" was popular in the colonial era. People wanting a keepsake placed a paper over a gravestone and rubbed with a soft crayon. They got an image this way. Do this with coins to see how it looked.

3. Read "Paul Revere's Ride" by Longfellow and "The Concord Hymn" by Emerson, two powerful poems about this period.

WINTER CAMP AT VALLEY FORGE

It's the winter of 1777–78 and you are with George Washington's army at Valley Forge. It's bitter cold. You remember the house you left when you joined the army. It was a nice warm farmhouse in Connecticut. You can just see the dancing flames in the fireplace. You can smell good soup cooking, bread made of rye flour and cornmeal. A cherry pie would be baking in the oven.

Here you are huddled in rags. This army hasn't even got uniforms. Your bare feet poke through your worn-out shoes. Your toes are numb with the cold. Your stockings are tatters. Your shirt and trousers hang on your body like strings.

How cold it is when the wind blows! How can you bear it any longer? The burning smoke from the fires makes your eyes water. If only you had at least enough to eat! But they only bring you thin soup. They call it beef soup, but where is the beef? The soup bowl is filthy. It is full of burnt leaves. But you must eat it. You try to get the awful stuff down your throat. Then you are deathly sick. You must vomit!

How can you stay here another night?

A fellow soldier leans close. He whispers, "Many are deserting. General Washington calls them 'sunshine soldiers.' He says they only stay when things go well. But I say only a fool would stay here."

Your eyes widen. You stare at the fellow. "Are you running home?" you ask.

"This night," he promises. And, true to his word, he disappears into the darkness. Soon after that another man cries out, "I am sick and lame! I am sore and starving! I am failing! I shall soon be dead!"

You joined this army because you love freedom. You believe in the cause George Washington is fighting for. But how much longer can a human being suffer so? There is no end in sight to bitter cold and food that is unfit to eat.

■ *If you stay at Valley Forge, turn to page 33.*

■ *If you leave, turn to page 34.*

Find out what your fate is!

31

You cannot desert no matter how miserable you are.

The next day some of the men find a pig. It is killed and roasted. At last you have a decent meal. But when it is eaten—and it goes quickly—there is hunger again.

"No meat! No meat!" the hungry soldiers wail. The owls in the trees seem to take up the cry.

A party is gathered to search for food in the countryside. The farms around here are poor. They will have little to share with you. But you must try.

You trudge through the snow until you come to a small farmhouse. When you rap on the door, a girl answers. She has big, scared eyes.

"Do you have chickens or a pig you might share with the boys at Valley Forge?" you ask.

"No, nothing!" the girl cries. "Other soldiers have been here. They took chickens already. We now have only enough for our own needs. Please go away." The girl slams the door in your face.

"Probably a Tory sympathizer," growls the fellow with you. "Probably hopes we all starve and the redcoats [British] win the war. She'd share quick enough if some redcoats came asking for food."

If you don't get some food soon, you will have nothing to eat tonight but firecake and water (flour and water).

"There!" your companion shouts, "There are fowl in the hen house! Let's help ourselves to some."

As you move toward the hen house, the girl comes out. "Do not touch our chickens! Are you common thieves?" she screams.

You feel very bad. You were not brought up to be a thief. But how can you and your companions get by without food? You would gladly pay the girl for her chickens. But you have not been paid. Washington cannot pay his own faithful troops! You have only a few coins.

"The boys are starving at Valley Forge," you say again.

"My own family is going without!" the girl answers in a hard voice.

■ *If you steal the chickens, turn to page 35.*

■ *If not, turn to page 36.*

Hating yourself, you sneak away from Valley Forge in the night. You are a deserter! But you could not bear the misery any more. Many are fleeing. You are not the only one.

You have a few coins in your pocket. You use them to get fresh clothing. Then you continue your journey home. You will tell your family you were sent home by the army doctor.

"I suffer from some lung illness," you will tell them. You will cough a few times. The smoke of Valley Forge is still in your throat. It won't be hard to cough.

Your family greets you warmly when you return. They praise you for giving so much to the cause of freedom.

But, as time goes by, you feel very guilty. Other men like you put up with the discomfort. Here you are, safe and well-fed and comfortable on your farm. You are haunted by the memories of your companions.

Besides, you believe in the cause you were fighting for. So when you hear of George Rogers Clark asking for volunteers, you go at once.

The Northwest needs to be defended against the British. In February of 1779 you march toward the western wilderness with George Rogers Clark.

Clark keeps everyone's spirits up by joking and telling stories. You are going to Vincennes, Indiana. You plan to attack and capture the British fort there. Then the Americans will control the Northwest.

You have to cross flooded land. For hours you wade through swamps and creeks. The water sometimes reaches to your shoulders. You must sleep in wet clothes. This is almost as bad as Valley Forge!

When you reach the Wabash River, no ship is available to take you across. For two days you are without food in the cold, wild land. Men talk of deserting again. But then Clark barks out an order. "All deserters will be shot!" You and the others build canoes to cross the river.

The capture of Vincennes is easier than you thought. The British General Hamilton sees your large force and just gives up! When you enter the fort you find much British wealth. Each of you get to keep a share!

Have you done enough fighting? Is it time to go home, or should you remain with Clark?

■ *If you go home, turn to page 37.*

■ *If you remain with Clark, turn to page 38.*

You snatch up two hens with the girl screaming at you, "Dirty, filthy thieves! What kind of men are you? Soldiers without honor!"

You toss the girl a coin and say, "We are men with hungry stomachs, Ma'am. Men living in the cold and dirt with nothing to eat."

You and your companions have taken six chickens and now you hurry back to camp. Soon the chickens are cooking over a fire. What a wonderful smell!

There is very little meat for so many hungry men. You could eat all six chickens yourself. But you must be glad for a leg. Some of the others get nothing but two wings. The remains of the chickens are cooked into a broth. It will be heated and reheated and served until it tastes like water.

You continue to see the angry face of the girl you stole from. (You gave her a coin, but far from the value of the chickens.) You will repay her in full when this war is over. You mark the debt in your mind.

A fellow plays the violin as the stars come out in the black sky. It's fine music. It reminds you of home and your family. When you weep a little, you blame it on the smoke in your eyes.

You fall asleep and dream of home. You are always warm and well-fed in your dreams.

You wake up once and see Doctor Waldo going into the hut where men are sick. The medicine is just grog—a mixture of rum and water.

The man who went with you to steal the chickens leans over. "Tomorrow we will get the hogs. They had two fine little hogs. And we'll take the rest of the chickens too," he says.

You know you cannot do it! You rise and slip from the encampment before dawn. You don't stop running until you reach Hyelyars Tavern. You offer to clean up there in exchange for a breakfast. Then, your stomach full of hot porridge, you hurry home.

The war rages on for another three years. George Washington is victorious and America is a new nation. You are proud of the part you played. But you are sorry you did not do more.

■ *Turn to page 39.*

You cannot take the girl's chickens! You hurry back to Valley Forge empty-handed. Your companions return with arms full of chickens. Soon the glorious smell of roasted chicken fills the air. But you must be content with firecake and thin soup.

The following night a man in the next hut moans desperately. You call Doctor Waldo. You hold the man's head up while Doctor Waldo gives him grog (a mixture of rum and water). But the poor fellow's cheeks are sunken in. His skin is clammy.

"I'm going," he whispers. He is one of the Indian soldiers serving at Valley Forge. He's been a fine, brave soldier. He is a Christian and now you pray with him. You promise to tell his family how bravely he served. When he gives a last shudder and dies, you are holding him in your arms. You gather his poor final effects to deliver to his family.

You manage to stay alive during the hard times at Valley Forge. You are surprised how strong you are. In January of 1778 you get leave. You can go home for a little while! You hurry from Valley Forge with your wages. (At last you got some wages as a soldier in Washington's army!)

You stop at a tavern and feast on honey and bread and oats. You feel like a king! Everything tastes so good.

After a short time at home, you go back to Valley Forge. There is more fighting and another cold winter camp. You are seriously injured in a bayonet fight in 1780, but you recover. You are there at Yorktown when the British General Cornwallis surrenders to Washington.

What an amazing day it is! The British bands play "The World Turned Upside Down." They cannot believe they have lost the war. You are so proud to see this moment. You will tell your children and grandchildren about it. You were there when the United States won its independence!

■ *Turn to page 39.*

You have served the cause long enough. Your enlistment is complete, and you head for home. Scrambling over hill and swamp, clutching your money, you go. With this money you hope to buy a farm in the West.

As you scamper over a field, Indian allies of the British attack you! Two warriors are hot on your trail. You money bag is heavy, and you must cast it away. Better to be poor and alive than rich and dead!

You hurl your bag into a bush and run faster. You dive into a lake and pretend you are drowning. When you finally peer out of the reeds, the Indians are no longer looking for you. They have gone to the bush and found your money bag!

Oh, no! You hoped they would go away and you could recover the money. Surely the Indians do not understand the value of the money. Their money is beads or shells. But they are taking the paper money from the bag!

You must remain in the tall reeds of the lake. You are wet and miserable. But you dare not show yourself.

One Indian has gone fishing farther up the river. He quickly catches fish. Then he runs to his companion. They twirl a stick and soon have a fire going. They are burning your money!

You watch in horror as the Indians broil their fish before the open fire. When they finally leave, you find they have burned every bit of your money.

With your stake gone, you decide to return to the battlefield. You fight against the British when they try to recapture the West in 1781 and 1782. In June of 1782 you are fighting under Colonel William Crawford at Sandusky.

A few weeks earlier some Pennsylvania settlers had killed ninety friendly Delaware Indians at the peaceful village of Gnadenhutten. Now all the Indians are on the warpath. The British are supporting the Indians. You are battling the Delaware, Shawnee, and Wyandot tribes.

On the upper part of the Sandusky River you meet Shawnee and Delaware warriors. It's a brutal one-day battle. You are among the fifty Americans who are killed.

■ *Turn to page 39.*

You remain at Vincennes with George Rogers Clark. You take part in many small battles. The British stir up the Indians against you. So sometimes you must fight British and Indian soldiers. Luckily, you always win. You grow to be a good friend of Clark's. You admire his courage and good nature.

When George Washington defeats the British in the last battle of the war, you are proud of the part you played. "Now what will you do?" Clark asks you.

"I will find a little farm and enjoy peace," you say.

"I may explore in the West," Clark tells you.

You hear from your friend, George Rogers Clark, from time to time. He tells you he has been asked to explore the Northwest, all the way to the Pacific Ocean. Nothing comes of it. You can sense that Clark is restless and sad.

You find just the farm you want in Ohio. Soon you are raising the finest apples in the state. You build a home and enjoy a good life. You often tell your children about George Rogers Clark. "He was the greatest hero I ever knew," you say.

When you have time, you visit your old friend. But each visit is sadder than before. It is George Rogers Clark's brother, William Clark, who is chosen to make the expedition to the Pacific Ocean. The hero of Vincennes is all but forgotten now. It is often that way with old soldiers, you think.

The last time you visit Clark, he is old and alone. He is living in Louisville, Kentucky.

"Look," he tells you, "I just got this gift in the mail."

You watch him open the large package. It is a replica of one of the swords he used in his famous battles. Clark's face turns red with anger. "When Virginia needed me to fight, I went to battle with my sword. Now all the thanks I get is a toy sword. I need bread, not toys!" With that he breaks the sword with his crutch.

You feel so bad. You remember the brave soldier of Vincennes. You remember how he led you through the darkest days. He was a true patriot. And now he is almost forgotten by his country. But you will never forget him.

■ *Turn to page 39.*

The Other Clark

George Rogers Clark was a rugged frontier soldier. He was a true hero in the Revolutionary War. His younger brother is even more famous, though. William Clark was half of the Lewis and Clark expedition.

In 1804–06 Lewis and Clark and about forty others left St. Louis and went all the way to the Pacific Ocean. They climbed steep mountains and crossed rushing rivers. Along the way they were helped by a brave young Indian woman named Sacajawea (Bird Woman). Among the explorers was a black man named York. The Indians along the way were very surprised to see a black person. They had never before seen anyone who wasn't either their own color or white.

The Lewis and Clark expedition opened the West for settlement.

True/False

———— 1. Among the hardships at Valley Forge was hot weather.

———— 2. Sacajawea is also called Bird Woman.

———— 3. George Rogers Clark and his men captured the British fort at Vincennes.

———— 4. William Clark was the son of George Rogers Clark.

———— 5. The Lewis and Clark expedition went to the Atlantic Ocean.

Menorah at Valley Forge

On December 25, 1777, the Americans at Valley Forge spent a cold, hungry Christmas. One of the soldiers was a young Polish Jew. He sat in his little hut and lit an eight-branched lamp. For it wasn't only Christmas. It was also the Jewish holiday of Hanukkah.

The boy began to pray. Suddenly a hand touched his shoulder. It was General George Washington. "What is that strange lamp, son?" asked the general.

"This is my Hanukkah lamp. It's called a menorah," said the boy. "Long ago a little band of Jews fought for freedom against a big army. God helped us. I think He will help us Americans too. That's what I pray for."

"You have lifted my spirits on this cold night, son," said Washington. "Long may your lamp burn!"

Matching

1. Valley Forge is in

   _____ .

2. The Polish boy's lamp was called a

   _____ .

3. The Jewish feast in December was

   _____ .

4. Deserters were sometimes called

   _____ .

5. Soldiers at Valley Forge suffered from

   _____ .

a) Hanukkah

b) sunshine soldiers

c) hunger and cold

d) Pennsylvania

e) menorah

Group Activities

1. Find Valley Forge on the map. It has about the same climate as Philadelphia. Look in an almanac and find the temperatures common there around January, February, and March.

2. Make a list on the chalkboard of the discomforts of Valley Forge. Discuss which of them was probably most unbearable.

3. On a large wall map, find these major battles of the Revolutionary War:
   Bunker Hill   Trenton   Saratoga   Kings Mountain   Yorktown

Invididual Activities

1. Pretend you are keeping a diary of life at Valley Forge. Make a comment about every day from December 14, 1777, to January 1, 1778. Imagine things that happened.

2. On a small map, trace the Lewis and Clark expedition.

3. Find pictures of the historic flags of the Revolutionary War period and draw them. Some excellent ones are:
   Continental flag (1775)
   Grand Union flag (1776)

   Bunker Hill flag (1775)
   Betsy Ross flag (1777)

TENNESSEE OR KENTUCKY PIONEERS

It's 1790 and you are a young pioneer moving West. Will it be Tennessee or Kentucky?

"I think Tennessee would be the place for us," your spouse says. "The corn fares well there. I have heard others say so."

"But the winters are severe," you point out. Your older sister lived in Tennessee for a while. Then she moved to Kentucky. "The snow piles deep in Tennessee. The streams freeze over. The canebrake was killed for miles." (Canebrake is dense growth of reedy plants.)

"But my relatives live in Tennessee," your spouse says. "They would help us get settled."

Your sister told you of the hills of Tennessee with pitch pine and white pine trees. She said the branches of the trees are like rubber. They can be tied into knots without breaking them. You suppose you could make a good life there.

Your spouse smiles and takes your hand. "I've heard the forests in Tennessee drop leaves and make a thick humus. The earthworms are plentiful. Crops should thrive there. But if you want to go to Kentucky, I will not argue with you."

You think it over as you pack your possessions into a farm wagon. You load your axe and auger (a long metal tool that looks like a screw, used for drilling holes in wood) and your adz (an axe-like tool for chipping timber). In go bags of flour, bacon, salt, and yeast. You slide in a spinning wheel, seeds, clothing, cloth, needles, pots and pans, and dishes. Very carefully you load on the family treasure—a grandfather's clock—along with a bureau (dresser) and a bedstead (a frame for supporting a mattress).

Driving your cows and horses before you, you move along the Cumberland River. At night you camp on the side of the road to fry bacon and cook biscuits over an open fire. Soon you must decide where your new home is to be.

//

- *If you go south into Tennessee, turn to page 43.*

- *Of you go north to Kentucky, turn to page 44.*

Find out what your fate is!

You arrive in Tennessee and find a good homestead. You girdle the trees (cut all around the trunk) with an axe. This will kill the trees. You need room to plant crops and build a house. Rising up the hillside are laurel slicks (urn-shaped pinkish-white flowers), and blueberries are growing everywhere. Your mouth waters at the sight of them.

You make a three-sided camp with poles. This must do until you build your house. You unload everything from the wagon except the grandfather's clock. The clock you will leave with neighbors for safekeeping.

You collect brush and chop down saplings with your spouse. Side by side you work to clear the land.

On the big day when the house is raised, neighbors gather to help. For lunch you feast on venison and biscuits and blueberry pies. The men roll logs to the site of the cabin. Then they lift them into place. Soon you have a real house!

You have worked hard planting the corn seeds you brought. Now you hope for a good crop. Until the corn grows you must live on venison and other wild game, plus berries you gather.

Once you shoot a bear! How proud you are. But the meat is coarse and greasy. It's not nearly as tasty as you hoped. "Ugh," your spouse says. "We should have left the bear alone. Now he's poisoning us!"

Now that your house is built, you want to bring the grandfather's clock to it. It will make the house seem like a real home! "I want to put it in our cabin," you say.

"No," your spouse argues. "Look at the windows! We have no glass, just oiled paper. It's not safe to have such a treasure in this cabin. It's much better if we leave it with the neighbors. They promised to take care of it until we have a good house with planed lumber."

The neighbors have a nice big house and the clock is safe there, to be sure. But you want it here, in you own home! "If it rains and the water comes in, we'll cover the clock. But don't you see, I am homesick in this wilderness. I want one piece of good furniture to look at!"

"Foolish!" cries your spouse.

■ *If you bring the clock home, turn to page 45.*

■ *If not, turn to page 46.*

You choose a homestead in Kentucky near a small creek. The neighbors help you raise a log house. Soon you and your spouse are busy planting the vegetable seeds you brought. The corn crop is very important. You plant it in rows three feet apart. Seven kernels go into each hole. When the plants grow, you will thin them out, leaving only the strongest. Then you will pick, shuck, and shell the mature corn. You will grind it in a hand mill or put lye on it to make hominy. (You soak the grains in weak wood lye to make hominy grits.)

Your older sister comes on a visit, bringing a fine gift—a hog. When the hog is killed, you will have smoked meat all winter.

One day, while your spouse is helping a neighbor with a family problem, you see a stranger in the front yard. To your shock, he is trying a steal a horse!

You make a great clatter of pots and pans in the hope of scaring the wretch away. You have heard horrible tales of bandits here who rob and murder homesteaders. You are a fair shot with the rifle, but you don't want a fight.

The man turns and grins at the house. He sees wash hung on the line blowing in the wind. He probably thinks you are greenhorns from the city. He is counting on whoever is in the cabin being afraid to come out. He goes right on stealing your horse!

You have no money for another team of horses. Without two horses you cannot pull the wagon to town. How can you get supplies?

You shout out the window, "Stranger, I have a rifle and it's pointing at your head! You get away from our horses right quick or you're in big trouble." You try to sound tough and confident. But your knees are knocking together. You have never shot at a human being before!

The man just laughs. He seems to figure if you meant to shoot you would have done it already.

You rush to the wall and take down the long-barrelled rifle. When you shoot at game you miss about half the time. If you fire and miss now, will he come running to murder you? Should you shoot at him at all?

■ *If you fire the rifle, turn to page 47.*

■ *If not, turn to page 48.*

You go off in the wagon and recover the grandfather's clock.

"This is a bad idea," grumbles your spouse.

"Oh, it will be so good to have the clock with us! I won't mind the bark shingles and the earthen floor so much," you say.

But your joy is short-lived. One day when you go to town to get supplies, a bear breaks into your cabin.

As you return with bags of flour and salt, you see the big dark creature lumbering out your front door! He has chewed through the leather door hinges.

"Look!" your spouse yells. "The bear has been inside our house! What if he knocked over the grandfather's clock?"

You say nothing as you jump off the wagon. The bear has already run back into the woods. You must see if the clock is all right. You race into the house and cry. "Oh, no!" While reaching for a bag of sugar, the bear knocked over the grandfather's clock. It is smashed on the floor!

"You see, you foolish thing!" shouts your spouse, coming in behind you. "See what your vanity has cost us? If you had been sensible, we would not have lost our dearest treasure. It would be safe with the neighbors."

You turn in anger. "It's your fault! You wanted to come to Tennessee! If we had gone to Kentucky as I wanted, we would not have to face hordes of bears!"

"Silly creature," snaps your spouse. "There are bears in Kentucky the same as here!"

You look down at the beautiful old clock. "I will always hate Tennessee. It is a harsh and wicked place!" you mutter.

You are yelling bitterly at each other when you hear a knock on the door. When you open the door, you see your closest neighbors. They are a young couple like you and your spouse. They hold their baby in their arms, wrapped in a blanket. Their faces are white and stark.

"She died in the night," says the young wife.

"Will you come with us for the burial?" asks the young husband.

The four of you stand at a pretty place under a tree. The baby is buried, and you all recite the 23rd Psalm together. You hug your neighbors then.

Suddenly the loss of your grandfather's clock does not seem so important. Hand in hand, you and your spouse go home to your cabin.

■ *Turn to page 49.*

You leave the grandfather's clock with the neighbors. But you resent it very much. This place does not seem like home. You are sorry your spouse won and you came to Tennessee. You are sure life would have been much nicer in Kentucky.

As you sit eating mush and milk for supper, you look around. "Hard-packed earth for a floor! Everything is so filthy. I hate it here. Bugs are everywhere! I think all the bugs of the earth must live in Tennessee!" you say to your spouse.

"We'll be putting in split logs first chance we get. After the crops are in," your spouse says.

Supper is over and you follow your usual routine. You spend the evenings carving wooden bowls and noggins (cups) and sewing. But tonight you don't say much to each other.

Most of your meals are made from corn: johnnycake, pone (bread made of cornmeal), and mush. "We won't have milk for our mush tomorrow," you grumble.

"Well, other folks make do with gravy or bear oil," your spouse points out.

"I will not eat mush with bear oil on it!" you snap. "I would rather go hungry."

The next day you must cook up fat drippings and alkali to make soap (the alkali is from wood ashes). Both of you carry the big buckets in the hot sun. How sorry you are you ever came to Tennessee! How bitter you feel!

The neighbors are going to town on Saturday. Their small baby has died of fever and they are very sad.

They ask you and your spouse to come along. You do not go. You are still pouting over the grandfather's clock.

Late in the afternoon, your spouse returns home.

"Did you get salt in town?" you ask. "I hope you at least remembered to do that!"

"Yes," your spouse says nervously. Then you see the bag of bright multi-colored hard candies. Oh! They are your favorite! But you dared not buy any. You have no money for such foolish luxuries.

You see a smile dancing in your spouse's eyes. "You longed for them, didn't you?"

"Yes," you admit. You grab a red one, your favorite, and it melts in your mouth. You smile at your spouse, and soon you are hugging each other. There are some things more important than grandfather's clocks, you decide. Like someone who loves you enough to buy a bag of candy.

■ *Turn to page 49.*

Poking the rifle through the window, you blast at the space over the bandit's head. He is just about to unlatch the gate. Now he jumps back. He runs behind a tree.

"Get out of here!" you shout. "I could have shot your head off. Next time I will."

"Listen, I'm no robber!" shouts the man. "I was just admiring your horses. I'm a horse breeder. I was just having a look at some good horseflesh."

You're no fool. You know a horse thief when you see one. A lawful citizen would have come to the door and asked to look at your stock. "Get off my land!" you shout.

"Just let me sit a spell under the tree. I'm real tired out. Would you have a sip of something cooling for me? I'd be obliged for some cool cider," he says to you from behind the tree. He is unshaven. He's missing a few front teeth. He's dressed in a dirty leather hunting shirt and pantaloons (loose pants). You can smell him this far off!

You fix your gaze on a branch over the man's head. You take aim and fire. The branch is splintered by your shot. Wood showers down on the stranger. He takes off running. He doesn't even look back.

Now you begin to shake. You put the rifle back in its place on the wall. When you needed to be strong, you were! Now that the danger is over, you are shaking all over. After all, you are a pioneer, not a gunfighter!

When your spouse returns, you ask, "How are the neighbors?"

"Fine now. They just needed a commonsense opinion to settle them down. I think I helped them a lot. Have you been keeping busy?" Your spouse seems proud of playing a part in solving the neighbors' problems.

"I tended the vegetable garden and made some candles. I plucked the wild turkey so it can be roasted. Oh, and I fired the rifle at a thief who wanted to take our horse. I expect he's still running!"

You laugh at the shock of your spouse's face. You now really feel like a brave pioneer!

■ *Turn to page 49.*

You cannot fire the rifle! What if you miss and the thief has a weapon and shoots back? He is surely better at gunplay than you are. He could blast his way into the cabin and murder you!

You watch in horror as the bandit steals your horse. He leads the animal into the woods and disappears. You run as fast as you can to the neighbors' house.

"Someone stole our horse!" you shout.

"What? When?" your spouse gasps.

"I saw the bandit from the window. He very boldly stole the horse. I could tell he was a fierce bandit," you say.

"And you did nothing?" cries your angry spouse.

"I was frightened. I took the rifle down, but then I could not fire! You know I am not a perfect shot. How could I know the man was not armed? If I shot and missed, then he might have attacked the cabin," you argue.

The men in the settlement hunt for the thief for the rest of the afternoon and early evening. No luck. Your horse is gone!

At suppertime you and your spouse sit at the puncheon table (made of cut-off logs). You have hog and hominy, but your spouse does not touch any. "If I had known how weak and afraid you were, I would not have come to the wilderness," your spouse says sadly.

"I am not weak and afraid!" you explode.

"You could have saved our horse and you did not! Pioneer people must defend themselves. There is not a sheriff here to help us! Now what will we do for another horse?" your spouse asks.

Sadly you walk to the corner of the room where the grandfather's clock sits. It is your only valuable thing. You love it dearly, much more so than your spouse does. "Will selling this bring enough for a new horse?" you ask.

Your spouse nods.

The next morning you sell the grandfather's clock. You ache with sadness to see it go, but it has to be. Silently you resolve what to do the next time you see a thief.

You must use the rifle.

■ *Turn to page 49.*

Pioneer Homes

The pioneer families in Kentucky and Tennessee were used to nicer houses. The harsh living in the wilderness was a big change. Furniture was homemade from wood. Mattresses were bags filled with straw. Covers were bear or buffalo skins. This bedding was usually filthy and filled with bugs. In the older colonies, people had wallpapered rooms, rug-covered floors, and beautiful mirrors. Canopy beds were clean and beautiful. Now the pioneers had bug-infested buffalo skins.

Little by little the pioneers made their homes in the wilderness better. The goal was a house of planed lumber, brick, or stone. When real window glass replaced the oiled paper, everyone celebrated. Lucky pioneers had big houses with many rooms and fine furniture.

Matching

1. The road to Kentucky and Tennessee was along this river:

   _____ .

2. Pioneer mattresses were filled with

   _____ .

3. Dense growth of reedy plants:

   _____ .

4. The rubbery Tennessee trees you can tie in knots are _____ .

5. Pioneer families considered one of these a treasure:

   _____ .

a) straw

b) grandfather's clock

c) Cumberland

d) canebrake

e) white and pitch pines

Group Activities

1. A Conestoga wagon was usually about sixteen feet long, four feet wide, and four feet deep. If you had to pack all your possessions into this space, what would you take and what would you leave behind? After everyone has made a list, the class should vote on the ten most often selected items, giving each item a ranking. For example, if the majority feels the television set is important, the TV would be number 1.

2. Using maps, find the major trails used for the westward movement into Kentucky and Tennessee.

3. Discuss what hardships you would have found most difficult as a pioneer in Kentucky or Tennessee.

Individual Activities

1. Your neighbors just helped you raise a house. You must make a fine dinner for them. Using foods mentioned in the reading selections only, write a menu for the feast.

2. Find a picture of a Conestoga wagon and draw it. Be sure to color it accurately. The running gear was bright red; the body, Prussian blue; and the cover, of course, white.

3. Find the seals of Tennessee and Kentucky in an encyclopedia. Notice how pioneer symbols appear in both.

Answer Key

1. On the Auction Block

    1. c   4. b

    2. e   5. d

    3. a

2. Servant for Sale

    1. b   4. a

    2. d   5. c

    3. e

3. Sons of Liberty

    1. F   4. F

    2. T   5. T

    3. F

4. Winter Camp at Valley Forge

    Clark:

    1. F   4. F

    2. T   5. F

    3. T

    Menorah:

    1. d   4. b

    2. e   5. c

    3. a

5. Tennessee or Kentucky Pioneers

    1. c   4. e

    2. a   5. b

    3. d